PRAISE FOR MICHAEL J. WILSON

"Michael Wilson's work shines." — *Publishers Weekly*

"The force that through the green fuse drives the flower Drives my green age,' wrote Dylan Thomas, in lines that kept echoing through my head as I read Michael Wilson's striking debut…*A Child of Storm* offers a stark and electric visual palette, as Wilson engages currents historical and personal, natural and made."
    — Dana Levin, author of *Now Do You Know Where You Are*

"Michael J. Wilson warns us "F*cking is unsafe" —as is love, as are public expressions of love in a homophobic world. The poems in *If Any Gods Lived* deliver to us the brutal complexities and emotional realities of intimacy and AIDS. Elegiac and life-affirming, unflinching, graphic, and utterly beautiful."
    — Denise Duhamel, author of *Blowout*

"Wilson is able to thread themes of desire, fear, shame, and grief together so masterfully I found myself unable to put the collection down."
    — Joseph Edwin Haeger, author of *Learn to Swim*

A LABYRINTH
Copyright © 2023 by Michael J. Wilson
ISBN: 978-1-960451-01-9
First paperback edition published by Stalking Horse Press, October 2023

Library of Congress Control Number: 2023942423

Publishing Editor: James Reich
Design by James Reich

Cover painting: *The Minotaur*, George Frederic Watts (1885)

Stalking Horse Press
Santa Fe, New Mexico

www.stalkinghorsepress.com

A LABYRINTH

ALSO BY MICHAEL J. WILSON

If Any Gods Lived

A Child of Storm

MICHAEL J. WILSON

A LABYRINTH

STALKING HORSE PRESS
SANTA FE, NEW MEXICO

Dedication

A LABYRINTH

1. SOME TAPESTRY OR OTHER

All stories begin with eyes opening.

Universes are born in the heat of someone seeing being seen for the very first time.

Those eyes become placed in a face that face becomes attached to a neck — some stories prefer their heads detached but those still begin with the eyes of a head in a basket carried through darkened hushed hallways before entering the velvet of night to be quickened into seclusion —

in either case —

at the start of all stories —

some neck with a face that has some eyes in it begins to turn —

    at first slowly
    then quickly
    then the eyes meet the world
    then the body names the world it sees hungrily.

In that moment even the world outside the story is changed.

It's in how those fictional eyes name and interpret the world where meaning begins to happen. Are the eyes blind or sighted to injustice. Is the night dangerous or calming. The head in the basket a relief or a threat.

A metaphoric author coaxes the eyes open — a metaphoric listener learns about those eyes is seen in them — all selves become stones tiled across a floor that stretches into a hallway that unfurls like a rug for as long as it takes. With that first opening — the cover of a book or first word spoken around a fire or in a rocking chair on a porch — potential is at its highest. The second there is a character to follow — that is the moment you are taken by the story down a path beyond your control.

Potential collapses. Paths become chosen others become unchosen. Doors close they lock are forgotten. You open your eyes first thing in the morning and name the world around you.

Here — for instance — a maze stretches like a cat rising from sleep at the sound of a can of food being cracked in the kitchen. First — the back legs — a good full spine get in there kind of stretch sending electrics down vertebrae — then the front — eyes closed in the feeling of it — this one is more about the legs neck shoulders. Then the eyes open — sigh — the world is bright again.

It's very good — this stretching thing.

The spine — all of the body really — is a thing resembling a ball of yarn. Something could be made — useful — could tie itself around the edge of the banister then drop bouncingly down the flight of stairs become a mess of itself. Bodies come in all the softest loudest

colors. But it is not only itself — it is the dye seeped in the fibers —
it is the plant or mineral the dye was concocted from. It is the hand
of the person who spun the fibers from the raw wool. It is also the
sheep alpaca rabbit animal itself meandering in some field. The rays
of the sun pointing its fingers into all of it as well. The expansion of
the universe and all those atoms doing their atom thing.

A miracle really. If there are to be miracles.
All things reflect other things.

The point is it is layered — as the end is unwound — more becomes
knotted to the end. The end is knitting along quickly it is as if it all
melted in a spring thaw a shelf of ice giving in to gravity. But it keeps
falling. Infinite shelves of infinite ice.

The looseness of some stories is a glory. That something so unbound
could still hold. A whole marvel. Some are wound around a core
that holds shape fast — makes a court of it. A scepter a mace placed
knightly within the yarn shell of protection.

The center could be a burnt plug of oak — deeply smelling of sulfur — a bad omen — an unbeating heart at the center of the skein. Finding unexpected but suspected darkness in the core of things feels very humanly.

Where do these cores come from — it seems to be heartwood — was at one point the veins of a tree — soft tissue — it carried sapblood from root to crown. It was the oxygen mover — the waste disposal system. It thrummed fungus in the earth about the tree's roots responded there was a kind of friendship among these things.

At some point a thing caused it all to come down to become a ball be hardened by fire then it was handled by the person who spun the yarn. You know this story —

yarn chasing through moss-covered deep underground hallways so a lover could slay a monster for love. It's a toy in your paws. You could tell it from memory. At the center of every story is an open mouth waiting to be fed. Children leaving breadcrumbs for themselves only to become lost in a wood faced with a witch then eaten for breakfast.

It is a stretching — stories are thankfully elastic — first the back —

Daedalus sits at a small wooden kitchen table. He is bothered.

Then the front —

Somewhere deep in the earth a monster awaits to be birthed.

It is the kind of stretch where a shoulder is sore stretching feels like it should help but in reality is probably tearing the fine pulp of muscle — the shimmering fishscale colors of fascia the tendon pulled a bit too tight. Maybe a hole will open up your arm will drop suddenly dead to movement. It might fall off. The sciatic nerve will make your leg go numb. Will kill your ability to walk. Maybe the layers of your skin will separate form a blister fill with water and flood you.

Best to lay on your back — close your eyes just for a moment imagine you are a cat lying in the sun — slow your breathing — be the floor.

You are the floor.

Breathe in.

                Hold.

Exhale.

Think about how the earth is beneath you — not even that far away — centimeters — a few meters at most — but also think about how people walk on you. How that is a gentle erosion. Within the earth there are things alive things that are not.

You must believe in the bedrock. In the successive layers of the skin of the earth.

Feel the tidal pull of the molten core of the earth. Not the myth of the hollow earth full of Titans — we must believe in something simple before something complicated. It is far simpler better factual to believe in the redhot core of a planet than a temperate internal utopia.

Stories come on you slowly like the lie of a frog in cold water that slowly reaches boil. Frogs feel temperature shifts just fine. They know they are about to die. They know you are killing them. All things know when they are to be destroyed.

Stories come like flood. The water level rises over the course of hours until you are under. At the beginning it's really simple. You see water. It's even interesting to watch it flow across places that are normally dry. Eventually you will be forced to see the depths it can reach. Unlike the frog feeling its end coming up — stories do not give away the moment you are about to go under. They hide this from you right until they have you by the neck.

Your fingers are heavy. Your toes — heavy as hell for it must be heavy if it is to withstand that number of souls. Feel your palms press into the floor — which is also you — as if into clay — also you. You could mold you into whatever you wish. You could make you into a likeness of you. Feel your arms become hot tar pooling. Your torso is an object filled with stones. You will sink slowly in the water like a body with stones in its pockets it is lovely you are lovely.

Now —
       breathe in.

       Hold.

       As you release — not yet —
       count slowly from ten to one.

       Ready —
       now
       release.

10

9

8

7

6

5

4

3

2

1

Open your eyes.

It is the kind of table everyone has.

It's for sipping coffee eating toast on a weekend morning while doing the crossword staring out at the songbirds near a feeder or the snow collecting itself quietly for kids hurriedly downing bowls of cereal before the school bus leaves — but in this small home without a studio for working — it has become a workspace. The surface worn shinydark from years of elbows arms plates.

In front of him — a pronoun — possibilities have shrunk — things must tighten in order to start. In front of him — the model of a Thing sits. Even at this size in this non-committal color in a kitchen filled with Monday morning — Daedalus knows.

Of course he does. Because the universe knew before it even knew that something was to be known — it knew before there were creatures capable of knowing it has hummed with it since the dawn of time.

It is in the sound of insects buzzing — birds calling each other at sunrise — the sound of waves rushing shore.

The Thing — a plan told in cheap available materials. The real — honest to version thing waits in the stones beneath Knossos to be birthed by picks muscles blood fear. Waiting for Rodin to free a lover's hands from marble.

Daedalus knows this is an idea he stole from the earth that this Thing in front of him that he has worked on for weeks is just the beginning of that idea that has always been there revealing itself.

Lost in the hallways of the model — he has been walking somewhere near the center — hand trailing along the cleanfresh walls. The sound of his fingernails scraping at the smoothness of the whitewash. An echo ahead and behind him. Ahead there is a bend to the right then a T. One way leads to a dark deadend that will eventually be full of moss insects bone. The other curves in what seems an endless turnless nothing that — he knows because he knows — is actually a winding corkscrew with the business end pointed at the center.

The Thing is designed to make you doubt yourself.

Suddenly — nothing is sudden — all things are just waiting for the right moment to pounce— an intersection with four ways.

This is the final test.
Only one leads to the heart.
The rest take you back to the edges where you will find a mirror of what has come before — an eternity of this most will die before they find — or are found by — the real horror within.

— You should eat.

She sets a plate in front of him — this second person went unnoticed until now but she was there. Eggs and some heavy bread. She is very pregnant with their first child — she holds one hand to the small of her back and stretches. Her left ankle is swollen and her lower back is a constant soreness. But she has watched him over days and nights as her body has expanded with the child. Zoe is tired from this watching.

He has been lost in these halls that he has made because after many weeks — today is the morning — the day — this Thing is to be shown to Minos.

Daedalus eats a spoonful of eggs.

Satisfied with that smallest of gestures — with her introduction — Zoe crosses her arms and leaves the room.

Where Zoe had been standing — there's an impulse to have had her leaning against a kitchen sink or counter. Anachronistic but the gendered coding in the placement seems difficult to push back from. A window would be behind her — the kitchen as archetype — curtains in pale yellowwhite gingham — made from the leftovers of a picnic blanket that they used on their first date.

They went to a parkland near the center of Athens.

He brought a jar of wine sandwiches in a small threadbare basket made from the same reeds that he sharpened into drawing styluses.

He claimed it had been a gift from a sister with a dead son Zoe would never meet.

The day was severely blue. There were swans in pairs on the small lake. Zoe thought of Leda and watched this man eat his sandwich.

She will never be able to decipher what he's thinking. Not in this first moment of knowing him — not in the last as she ceases to breathe while he dumbly watches her die — her blood flowing as if a river had broken free from within her. More blood than you would think could be in one body. Everything she ever was absorbing into the fine rugs of a palace room. Staining the stone beneath. A thing to be covered until the palace itself was destroyed by time.

His eyes betray only the rapid spinning of spokes on a chariot — the key embedded on his back has something to do with this — a small sigil of birthmarks in the shape of a key — he has always said this was the source of his power — and once unwound — his end.

The wide park had been her favorite place since she was a child. Zoe would take her older sister's hand they would come hide seek tag.

It was a dry summer the year they met. She had been working in a bakery. Her father had died at sea. Her mother Iris was collecting a pension from the merchant's association for the loss of Linus — he had been a very successful captain manager on a main shipping route. Her sister Airlea had married was thinking children — wearing only the sharpest white to pluck good omens from the air — she burned sage beeswax at homemade altars to Leto to Venus. She ate candied violets the too sweet scent a constant about her.

Daedalus was already Daedalus. Had maybe always been so. He was enough himself that she knew him by his name when he placed his order. The famous inventor of carpentry the saw axe plumb-line drill glue isinglass. The idealist who thinks ships could have tree trunks rising from them with massive kites of fabric to catch wind to pull them across the entirety of the seas.

All of it bullshit —
        but a lovely pile.

To think that this man in his mid-20s was responsible for things that had come into being hundreds of years before. But this was to be the way with him. Credit poured into his lap like wine into cups. The wealthy famous sat alongside him and held his hand — hoping that his artistry would make them more interesting in the process.

Credit has a way of collecting interest — in winding tunnels that bore downwards into the hot core of the earth — like acid on bone. Like it had always been there waiting in the praise to be realized. The eggs of a cuckoo laid in the nest of another.

He ordered one loaf of bread. She wrapped it for him. He left.

The simplest of gestures — those are the ones that make things go permanent. You hand someone something they say thank you and then you are in love. Of course it takes much longer — but that spark — it's like rubbing twigs on shredded cotton. This is always how it happens.

It had been eighteen months since the knock at the door in the early morning. The sun hadn't even bothered to rouse itself mists still hung around the whitewashed walls of the city. Athens is dumb in summer — but in fall becomes lovely. Of course bad things happen in lovely seasons.

Airlea was at the door first. She had been up all night — her sleeplessness fixed in her since birth. She would sit near the old fat lamp embroidering flowers onto linen. She would take the results to the women at the market get drachma. She had a small clay jar she dropped them into. What she saved for was beyond Zoe — though Airlea now had a nice house nice cloth and a few other things that seemed to not come from her husband so.

The man at the door was dressed for warmer weather — a young messenger from the trade guild. One who was not used to early hours by the look of him. He entered the house nervous like he was coming home to his parents after a night of drunken stupidity. He seemed confused as to why he had come to this door at this hour. Was he here to rob these women. His face was red. He was a redundancy.

28

— I am sorry for arriving so early.

Both Zoe and Iris had come into the room. Zoe in her nightclothes. Iris with an ornate coat over her robe nameless look on her face. This was an odd way of starting business of any kind. What is the use of being sorry if you are already there.

The messenger fumbled with the fob of his keys. So many keys. They hung at his waist — as if the very gates of the world were in his control. They were keys to the various storage lockers that he was tasked with checking each night before leaving for home. On this night — he had been stopped by someone told to run this errand or be docked pay. So here he was.

— I'm here about Linus — his status — the status of him — Linus —

His fumbling was distracting even himself — he spoke in halts creating gulfs of whitespace where anything could have happened. He was remembering that he had not finished his checks. He wanted to turn go back to the docks to safety away from these women with their eyes.

He sighed deeply — eyes moving down to the floor to the wall to the color of the rug. He sighed a second time the impatience of the three women in front of him filled the space. It felt buoyant. His feet were about to leave the ground.

— I have news of him.

Iris narrowed her eyes. Something creeping up her spine. Zoe could feel the room cool as if a fire had gone out. She turned to the fireplace to see and realized that it had been cold for hours.

The finished embroidery Airlea had been working was on the small ledge near the door where the family left notes for each other. Where letters messages things collected before being sent to the right person. Intricate purple crimson egg yolk birds spiraled against the soft white of the linen. They held white roses in their mouths. They had white rose petals for eyes.

Beside it — quiet — one large iron key — the sign of luck that Linus left in that spot every time he left on a business trip — a key to signify his return — he would point it to sea while away — to the hearth when he was there.

It was slightly off center — not quite in the spot it normally sat. The messenger looked from the women to the key then back to his own keys as if this was one he also needed. As if it had escaped his ring. The machines of his mind tried to assemble a lock for it to go in.

The quiet was going on too long.

— There has been news —
                                        a — an — ah —
                    at sea.

The word sea has always meant fierce wild thrashing. It has always meant here there be dragons. Churning face of wine. Innate fear held within its sculpted surface.

Iris was becoming angry with the slowness of the man and she said so. He startled everything suddenly clear as water in a glass. As if water itself was speaking through him.

> An accident.
> Destruction.
> Burning holes in fabric.
> Eighteen months in one second.

The sea is suffocating rolling danger.
One large body pressing against the scream of the landscape.
A density alive.

Airlea quickly married left the house — a father's death is a perfect excuse to push plans forward or back — the jar of drachma went with her — the key stayed pointing outwards. Zoe began at the bakery — to escape the sadness of the immovable object at the door. The waxen walls. The mother insisting on old rites of blacking windows mirrors eyes.

Grief collapses time. In a blink it is years later — everything feels the same but through twisted colored glass. Reflections of reflections of reflections. It is hard to understand the world when it shows itself to have no need of you.

Zoe's mother had only just taken the black off the mirrors the week Zoe met Daedalus — had only just stopped washing every surface with seawater and hyssop — her skin welled puckers from the cleansing. A permanent sea barely contained within her. She smelled of salt air. Her skin translucent from refusing the sun. At times it seemed her hair was full of shells her neck tensed with the open close of unseen but definitely there gills.

Bakeries are a constant mourning. The yeast that you cultivate raise you must give up must become Chronos must continue. Meditative kneading. The dryness of flour. Mixing. Death for sustenance rebirth the cycle continuing to roll downhill to be pushed up once again.

Zoe didn't actually make the bread — slicing bagging writing the sign out in chalk on the front wall of the building were her jobs. It was thoughtless. She said the same three things to every person. Which one price thank you.

She dressed in dark blue linens stood watch at the counter. The baker was a kind man named Hoddus who talked about baking as if it was the perfection of creation itself.

> You must make things twice —
> > first to learn —
> > > second to perfect.

Hoddus' wife was Iris was taking care of a newborn. Zoe knew them from the area — it was a kindness that they offered her this position.

Daedalus left with his loaf. Came back the next day.
    The next.
    The next.
    Asked Zoe to have lunch with him.

The sandwiches were made from the bread she had sliced for him that morning. The wine was dark clear sweet Zoe did not know its origins in all likelihood Daedalus did not either.

She thought about swans — about Leda — they sat on the old blanket that had been her mothers. That had been the blanket that she her sister her mother her father had sat on in summers in this park to eat lunch. A blanket that a grandmother had made for the birth of a daughter. No one remembered which or when.

Zoe does not know how to sew.

A skill that would suit her well if the bad times that hung around them in the current moment of the Thing and the elbow worn table were to continue. She thought back to Airlea — her embroidery — tried to remember the steps from yarn to drachma. They hid from her as she focused on them.

Her unbleached linen eddies around her legs as she exits this room to the bedroom. Only her back is seen — layers of the fabric pull glide across the muscles of her shoulders. There is a wave — flit of the eye — a bird vanishing into a denseness of trees — blue red soft butter yellow — a bee eater on the hunt. The scent of honey synesthesia. It is possible to spoon it onto bread. Zoe wears pepper and violet. She places it smoothly on her neck wrists. The olive oil base glistens on her for hours.

The kitchen in the house of Daedalus was without windows or sinks. House of Daedalus implies that the home is something that it is not. This was exile. This was fix-the-problem-or-die.

The railroad of entrance area to kitchen to back bedroom was in the middle of a block of small spaces in the most forgettable corner of Knossos.

Even if she had known how. And had the blanket that was most likely with Airlea in Athens. And there had been windows to do anything with — there were hopes of leaving this place as quickly as possible. Zoe had refused to unpack anything in the eight months they had been there. Cases sat unopened near the bed.

She walked from the kitchen into the small sitting room that was also the bedroom. Light was creating an aurora around the rough brown curtains on this window — the only window — these curtains were here when they arrived — she realized they should have been washed immediately but pushed the thought away. What does one do in this kind of room in the early morning. The options — sit on the bed or on the trunk at the end of the bed. The options — stare at the whitewashed walls or the whitewashed ceiling. Obsess over getting out or obsess over being here.

Artists and scientists are lawful though neutral. Believing wholly in themselves their right to ignore everyone else — their feelings — as long as their work continues is received by someone grows.

Lawful in that there is a clear sense of right and wrong in them.

Neutral in that they will not flinch if another is pained by their virtue.

At some point Zoe had fallen in love with the idea of Daedalus. Had gone along with it — why yes he did invent the sail — of course he came up with isinglass — yes he can make wood rock metal sing with only the power of his mind.

Such bullshit.

Of course he had made glorious statues. They lined galleries in great palaces. Were written about drawn endlessly copied by other lesser workshops.

Of course he had designed great buildings objects his recipe for isinglass was a massive improvement but —
        at some point —
                even before they had married —
                        being Daedalus had replaced actual work.
He made plans but those passed to hands of assistants collectors governments. Zoe was unsure of the last time he held any tools at all. Before the Thing she had forgotten he knew how to actually glue things together.

Five years ago on the invitation of a guildmaster Zoe and Daedalus had come to Knossos. That guildmaster had been the investor on her father's final voyage. She only knew him by name. If he even remembered her father or that trip at all there was no way that he knew who she was.

Zoe remembered everything. Her earliest memory was of moonlight reflecting off a mirror onto the ceiling of the room she slept in. She must have been two. It looked like water magic. There were crickets singing in the night and light played over the plaster like it couldn't find a place to hold still. She remembers this because the moment calmed her but also troubled her. Those slipping movements were not to be trusted.

On that first night in Knossos Zoe sat at the dinner listening to the investor rattle off his investments his ties to great things how Daedalus would be the latest great thing he was tied to. She was waiting for him to speak to his losses. Which — of course — he never did.

Daedalus built him a new kind of timekeeping device.

On their second week in Knossos the invitation to the palace came. The King of Crete himself wanted to meet the man who made statues walk down the hallways of Athens.

Even after becoming accustomed to the sort of people who circled her husband Zoe was still excited to put on her nicest cloth and peek in the archways of the rich. Her father was not a merchant — not really. He was the man merchants hired. His ship was a guild's. His money was a percentage. While he was respected — sought after — even somewhat famous in certain circles. He was a maker — not an earner — of wealth.

The house of Linus in Athens had many windows. A courtyard even. It was near the baths.

Daedalus though.
He was taken care of.
Not rich.
Literally housed fed clothed.
Kept.

By virtue of that love — Zoe too — was now taken care of.

Becoming used to — expectant of — that behavior was a surprise to her.

She wrapped that fine cloth around her body. Knowing that is wasn't hers — while still being hers. She had taken to putting select things in her traveling chests just in case they had to sell items to make a living. The chest she now sat on was one of them.

The current state of Daedalus and Zoe — wife of Daedalus — was precarious. This Thing he was building was a last effort to see things right. The great mistake of Daedalus — she considered it the first but it was really the second of many. A kind of inflammation about the joints of her body. A concern in her unborn child who would grow to be a great doctor.

She thought of the wife of Minos. What must she feel in all of this. The horror of it all. She pushed this from her mind — she had only been told of the horrors — her mind had filled in the detail. Her view of the world was tilted with it — how could such broken things exist. And that her husband had pushed the hands of fate in the creation of these broken things.

Her mind went to the fine peplos she had worn that first night in the palace of Knossos that now was folded in the chest she sat on and how many coins it would fetch today or tomorrow. It was natural linen with a bright blue edge. She had worn it to first meeting with the King of Crete.

— This is some tapestry or other. It came from the people east of Antolia. My father acquired it.

I've never been a fan of the design so fortunately it is in this hallway where I rarely come across it.

I'm sure it's worth a lot.

An implied shrug.

King Minos II — son of King Lycastus — son of King Minos I — son of etc. etc. etc. A certain amount of etceteras appear in certain kinds of stories. Minos II's mother was taken to Crete by Zeus himself in his shining white bull form. She was his consort. A direct lineage to Zeus godself.

Zoe looked at the tapestry. A dragonlike serpent a mountain rising from a sea an expanse of clouds. She reached out to touch it — the pile was clearly fine silk she wanted to bury her fingers in it.

She did so.

There was no dust it smelled fresh. How often this thing despised by its owner must have still been taken down to be beat upon on some balcony. Perhaps there was a servant who was punished if they were not constantly taking down tapestries whose owner despised them to thrum them against a balcony.

Minos was leading them around some hallway. Pointing out the riches of Crete — his riches — attempting to say that all of this rivaled Athens herself. Zoe was sure Minos' lineage was very impressive what with the tapestries and all — but she also knew his family was in power because they united Crete under one banner then conveniently erased everything that came before.

The first Minos had actually been a power hungry soldier who maneuvered to overthrow the former ruler after he had united the governors of several districts behind him. The plot had led to the former ruler being stabbed into ribbons in a field just outside of Knossos. Minos II's mother had indeed been — taken — to — Crete — but it was by his father in a bargain to reaffirm trade with Phoenicia — though there could have been a great white bull involved — if there were it was probably Zeus because why not —
everything is Zeus if you try hard enough. He could be blamed or championed for everything everywhere if one squinted just a bit — tilted their head to the left and willed it so.

Being cut to ribbons. Skin and blood turned into party streamers. Strips of fabric hung around flagpoles in spring. An image of flesh made into a pleated lantern filled with air set into the night sky.

That his mother and father were also related —

                                       however distantly —

                  was left unmentioned.

                  Except by those who loved to mention it.

But that wasn't unusual.

In some fine room dressed in dark velvets Minos showed them a bed that was made from one tree trunk. It was polished a syrupy orange color. The walls were green. The carpets were greenpurple. Everything was a jewel. The room looked out onto a balcony. The light outside was a hot white wash. The salt of it hit her in the face — she felt very much alive.

The men were talking.

— These would be your rooms —

        If you agreed.

Without even looking her direction Daedalus agreed.

Outside the window expanse of gardens. Several leucist peacocks paraded for each other. Zoe locked eyes with one. She had always thought of peacocks as pretentious having airs being bitches. This one seemed to be filled with sadness. The two gray marble eyes swirled with heaviness.

It all felt very much like a story she had been told as a child. Like the echo of something that maybe had not happened yet. The room was echoing with a fable that was just out of reach of her.

To love a narcissist is to be turned slowly to stone.

Daedalus spoons eggs to his mouth.

Stares at the blank table in front of him.

The sound of his patron in his head — to him anger had always been a sickly yellowgreen smell of sour breath why so many saw it as red eluded him.

He is barely aware that his wife has left the room.

The rough-drawn sketch of the Thing was spread on the table next to the wood model — drawn on an ornate napkin Minos had stuffed into Daedalus' shirt on a Friday eight months ago before sending him to this place. Eye to eye — the King of Crete slowly fed the linen napkin into the neckline of Daedalus' shirt. Smiling like a crow the whole time.

The stuffing of the napkin came after Minos had yelled for hours — my Queen who do you think you are — pacing in front of a large mural of a woman pouring wine for an army of people as Daedalus sketched frantically on the surface of the fabric.

In another room of the palace — nearly forgotten though how could he be — a child slept silently on a cot in a bare room that might as well have been a cage.

Daedalus doesn't know what to call it. His Thing. He cannot stop calling it the Thing. It will take ten years to unearth. Then many more to be undone. Though it will never really be undone. One cannot unwrite. Not fully. The page remembers.

Many many centuries later the men who built the first nuclear weapon called their creation a Gadget. A distancing device. As if it were a wind-up toy. In many ways it was. In many ways so was this.

Like the Gadget this Thing was the solution to a new problem. It is possibly the invention of a problem and a solution in one. A new spring come up from within the crust of the earth bubbling forming rings of colored minerals — an eye geyser a star that draws a crowd to it at specific times of day.

Once it is built — on the solstice of each season Minos will pull the people of Knossos into a plaza he will make from a field behind his palace. That plaza will remain closed off behind large golden gates large hedges the sound of wind that circles it. The grass within will be terraced will be paved at the bottom where the radiating circles of stone will point their fingers at the maw of the earth screaming the pain left over from the birth of the universe.

Minos will stand motionless while the children of Knossos and Athens are tossed into the hungry earth. He will demand his wife Daedalus

Zoe stand there as well. The children of Minos. Of Daedalus. Any courtesans lords gawkers. All will be made to stand. The sun will be relentless everything will be relentless to look at. They will watch children be led into darkness.

Then Minos will go watch his daughter dance.

As Daedalus eats his eggs — his eyes measure the difficulty in walking the hallways. He has traced to the center of the model and out eighteen times. Each time he has tried to path each hall. He has been unable to do so. Even in designing and tracking it with his eyes — he is barely able to remember where the true path assembles itself.

In Athens he was a child then a youth then an apprentice to a master builder. A carpenter engineer. His master was a man that history has forgotten — Daedalus is content in agreeing that his abilities are innate not teachable that he was birthed with them and has never had a master.

His hand traces the lines of the drawing on the napkin.

— You will one day be the best of designers.

Voice of the master — gravel in water — a soon to need oiling clockwork.

       — You have already found a way to improve this design.
       You see the flaw in the wheel. You reach to smooth it.

The design is old — something that was never built. A series of
cogs that — in unison — make the face of a device that tells the
story of time. A clock. Dumb in its design — useless.

Daedalus sees in lines. Every surface a series of undulating fields. The
world in slices stacking endlessly until they reveal form. An object is
only radiating topography. Take the hand —
      the mountains of the knuckles —
            circular lines spiral down the flesh pool at the
            shallows between fingers.
      They are heat marks — ripples in water.
Every hand is a radiating series a cascade of flesh.
The palm is marshland filling with cereals.

The back a wide expanse of prairie where the largest beasts roamfeed.

Outside of the human self these lines drop off corners snake into the world forming every object along the way — an unbroken line pushing. A trail left behind as if from a snail — as if from the cutting of a boat across the Mediterranean.

Every surface is an eye.

When he was a child he went missing for a few days into the farmlands around Athens. It was just after harvest time. The light at mid-summer is highbeam — a chalk outline — it is withering flush. Everything bleaches into the color of sandstone.

When it happened — the start of it — the going missing — missings come in stages of inevitabilities. To go missing — one must be in the right place at the right time. There is the part where there are signs — where the world begins to click over the various layers of being and the right people end up in the right places.

When Daedalus' missing started he was standing near the fields —
it actually started when he had decided to go to the field or when
the trees was cleared two centuries before or when grains were first
planted — the pieces moved around until Daedalus was watching a
group of carrion crows pick at a dead rabbit. They were not fighting
in the normal way. They were taking turns. Were watching each other
take turns.

From that rabbit — splayed to ribcage — veins of an umbrella that
the wind had torn the fabric from. The crows stood — four of them
— spokes on a sun cross. Each a cardinal direction point.

The one to the north — color of ash
        after a house fire — feathers tipped white darts.

                The eastern one turned bronze
        pattern arose there — gold left behind after
mercury burned away.

South is always sea — closest to Daedalus
      the one with its back to him. The last one — western
            stood in a stance that told Daedalus this one was
            the leader

      directing the moment — the oldest — graying the temples
it had journeyed far in this world.

From them — the lines of the cardinal sped in their directions to the edge of the world — off of it into the concentric spheres of space. They pierced the heavens continued into the lands beyond where even gods and monsters couldn't dare to guess what lived. They spun webs between the pin pricks of light in the celestial dome and brought the idea of constellations into being.

A crystal place. Where light bent on itself became dark. Refraction. There Daedalus couldn't see. Lines became arcs became blobs of matter turned inward on themselves then vanished. Daedalus abhorred an ouroboros.

The lines drew the child Daedalus forward. Into the field. Crows are tower birds. Watchbirds. Their eyes are a crosshair. The crows watched as he approached them — their burning center of the sun. They opened their circle to admit him. They closed around him.

Five days later — dehydrated starved — the child would be found by a farmer on the opposite side of the city from where he began. Perdix — his older sister — had not closed her eyes or even blinked for the duration.

After his apprenticeship was over — Daedalus opened a shop of his own. Designing the things that others would build. The frustration of watching a perfect design turn into an imperfect object. The hands of others a sad substitute to the ones in his mind.

So he turned to building himself he hired his sister's son Talos to help. Two coins a week and Daedalus taught Talos. Talos arrived with great natural talent.

Daedalus — in his 20s — before he met Zoe — before he was famous — but only just — he had Talos as his hands and eyes.

They made devices for the rich. They drew plans for buildings contraptions diversions. A carriage that moved without horses by compressing bellows with the feet. They improved a process for isinglass. They found ways to make elaborate wooden joints.

Daedalus' name was growing across the city. He was commissioned to make a series of statues that moved their arms into poses for the imperial palace. Not by anyone important. But by the people who did things for important people.

The statues that walked — the idea of a forgotten man who was in charge of filling empty corridors in one of the many aristocratic houses of Athens. They would be wood marble bronze — they would realign their arms when asked. This idea was brought to the doors of the workshop of Daedalus — the idea passed to Talos. Talos made them real.

You should never go into business with family.
Or lovers.
Or friends.
Really with anyone.

Talos drew the plans and the machinations inside them. The arms would reposition from the viewer to the heavens. They would move from human to godly with the press of a lever at their side. Joints of oiled wood — arms of worked metal — bodies of marble stone. Awe inspiring — magic in the way science can be magic.

Talos built a third secret into these statues.

An extra push on the lever — the statues could lift one leg at the knee press the foot down a full step ahead.

Magic comes in many forms. The sun alone casts several forms of it on the surface of water. That light on the ceiling of Zoe's room when she was a baby. The moment that a baby grasps a finger. There is a second in spring — only one really — but it feels longer — where everything is just about to rebear itself to life. The buds are still tight fists of anticipation. The air has yet to soften. The light is crisp. That one second where you know that in another everything will shift. Because it does. The light will change the buds will pop their seams the spring will have released its tension.

Magic isn't for magicians — they only play with it. It is not in creators either — they capture it in glimpses but do not control it. It is a spying game for them. A freezing of time that can be seen by others. Writers have this gift as well. All magic appearing things are just freezing moments then calling attention to the pre-existing perfection.

While Daedalus is not a magic holder — he is a seer. Talos on the other hand —

— And now

The space was filled with the rich of Athens. A hallway really though — packed to the rafters. Another phrase that when examined feels odd. Each of these rich were in their finest. Each with wine glass held high. That forgotten underling — who had commissioned these things — was smiling largely at the front of the eyes of the crowd. A form under a cloak next to him.

— Now we shall see what young Daedalus has come up with!

This is the moment.

They exist across time. When something someone crosses the stream into a kind of fame that becomes a kind of myth. Once they were a person a being who had muscle blood fear. Then they did one simple thing. Only a simple thing works but it must appear unsimple. Then they become more than. Extra.

The cloak was pulled back —

Athena.

She stared softly at the group. Everyone was silent. Unsure what to make of this. She held her hands out. Seemed to want to cradle each

of them — pull them to her — mother them. The mix of materials
— ugly cacophony — painted brightly for the dark hallways — it was
not there then it was there. Glass eyes glazed with tears.

The forgotten man smiled
                    he kicked the lever with his foot.

Her gaze unchanged but her arms shifted up at the shoulder elbow.
They turned. They rose into a stance of victory. A call to arms. She
may as well have drawn a sword lit a torch to war.

Everyone gasped.

Then that unremembered man hit the lever again —
                    Athena lifted her knee took a lurching step
                    forward her body leaning slightly onto her
                    outreached foot.

                    Her gaze menacing —
                    she would attack.

The crowd recoiled.
A man fainted.

Magic is really just not understanding what is being seen. Trick of the brain. Everything could be magic. This is why no one can hold it. They can only hope to communicate what they saw.

What happened next is fairly obvious. Cheers to the boy maker. Cheers to Daedalus —
        — and to Talos.

That specific and is where everything falls apart.

Were Daedalus a good man — he would have been content to fill Athens with walking statues build ever larger wonders — with Talos at his side.
                  That pause implied in the punctuation.
The glottal stop.
        The gag.
     It's a bad taste rendered tangible in letters on a page.

It means that we all know Daedalus is not that man.

Sin is something you either believe in or not. It is a creeping place of goalposts that can move and realign at will. Moderation seems to be the wisest course. In all things. Even sin. Pride greed sloth gluttony lust wrath apathy vainglory envy — at their best these emotions would move us to be better. Little doses of poison that immune us to the larger floods within and without.

Daedalus — was filled with envy. It boiled a sickly milk under his heart — pale beyond the point of being identifiable — blooming into him with the fibrous spores of underground mushrooms waiting to pop to the surface with the damp of early fall. It tickled him — plucked his strings at the first and last of the day. A communication that even he was sometimes unaware of.

Talos the draftsman was asked to draw for a well-known architect. Talos the draftsman was asked to recreate some mechanical device that had been forgotten to history. Talos the draftsman created a second third fourth fifth walking statue for that same homely hallway where Athena had come to life.

Of course he did — of course words were moving around gossipy Athens that Talos not Daedalus — was the gifted one.

Zoe never met Talos.

Talos is dead.

Daedalus walks the hallways of the Thing with his eyes. His foot kicks a bone along the floor of it. It makes a hollow dry wood sound across the rock. Across the wet moss. It rests in the corners. Daedalus wonders how a bone got into his Thing.

In the workshop. One year after the triumph of Athena. A year of moving statues. In the history of such a place as Athens what is one year. One life.

In the workshop
a tension — the way spring
is tension the way — a child
is a tension.

Talos bent over his work. Who cares what it was he was working on — something polished magical that Daedalus barely understood — but it was a statue of Hermes. The figure stood half-made nearby Talos was making the machine. By this time Talos' work had begun to seem like magic even to Daedalus — who knew how it was made. What was built. The insides. When even the knowledge of how doesn't prevent something turning into magic it is time to find a new science.

Daedalus had watched the drafting attempted to absorb the lessons in the watching but had come up empty. He looked away and refused to look back.

Talos' objects had begun to breathe.
At night.
At day.

The sound of it — bellows pressing themselves up down. Barn owls ghosting in the night. Noise of fire. It was a ticking inside of Daedalus' heart. Murmuring. He picked up a length of wire.

Look.

There are things known unknown in this world.
The wire probably cut into the skin around the neck.
Most definitely bruised.
Talos was younger so he definitely fought back.
Daedalus had to take him to the floor of the workshop.
Into the wood shavings that padded the bare earth.
He might have reached for a hammer or an awl.
Or maybe Talos reached for it instead — legs kicking pinwheels —
hands trying to magically undo the tightness across him.
Maybe he got a swing in.
Maybe the tool hit Daedalus.
Maybe even drew blood.
But not enough.

Oddly — they both thought about winter in that moment. Frost on
landscape. Fields fallow waiting for spring to bring the barley out.
Talos thought about the feeling of wetness in the bones. Daedalus of
the quality of light — how accurate ice is.

Then the lack of oxygen. The grotesque staring of the unfinished Hermes. The messenger unsent.

A blanket smothering everything. It does not snow like that in Athens but winter is a blanket over everything no matter where you are. A time of pausing.

Talos tried to speak — twist his eyes to meet those of his uncle — they were not so far apart in age for the understanding to not pass between them — the eyes looked like his mother's — Perdix did not close her eyes for five days — Talos stopped kicking.

People still asked for more of the walking statues after. Daedalus refused — saying that they were meant to be exclusive for specific persons he would never do that again. He would feel strange working on them without his beloved nephew.

The wire was cut and used to make a device that commemorated the life of Talos it sits on Perdix's mantle to this day or at least Daedalus assumes so. That Daedalus thought gifting the murder weapon to the mother of the victim was good or right is a tell.

Perdix discarded it soon after it was given to her. She knew — in the back of the neck where the feeling of encroaching evil lives. She knew she refused to speak to Daedalus in this world or the next. At night she would bind unbind the hands and feet of a small doll made in the likeness of her brother. She would do this for ninety days then burn it make another.

The workshop filled with new apprentices new draftsmen then more orders of mostly small household things and then Daedalus was taken care of. Not one of the new apprentices was any good. This was a requirement.

One day Daedalus began to notice the woman working at the bakery near his home. And then he began to buy more bread. And eventually he took her to a picnic lunch of sandwiches and wine he had been gifted by an artist of renown in a park that he liked nearby.

He is lost again inside the Thing. The center of it is a sun cross he cannot find the pathway to the pathway to the spokes.

Zoe smooths the fabric over her belly. The baby turns itself. It will be born within the month. Will be named Iapyx. Will become a doctor in order to heal the pain that sat in the womb while he made himself.

Outside the day is getting going Daedalus has an appointment with the King Zoe wonders to herself if this is better than selling bread and wearing rough linens. She thinks of her mother now living in the house of her sister. The old house gone to others.

Daedalus is concerned with his reputation — a broken field where a temple once stood — the sound of no strings on a harp — a hand without a body floating in space.

Five years ago he actually made something on his own with his hands for the first time in years something marvelous terrible.

He built a bull.

So now he must build another Thing to cage the thing begat by the thing. To compensate for the first. To regain what was lost. Or try.

Or even begin to attempt.

He moves the string only he could see that had tied his thinking to the Thing and it comes loose. The chair makes that sound chairs make against hard floors as they move beneath you. That movement makes the skull resonate with sound.

He is standing. Is turning his head because he knows it is time and in a moment there is a knock at the door.

Zoe smooths her fabrics pulls open the curtains in the room. The space fills with light that is difficult.

— Bullshit

Out loud —
        but to herself.

2. ONE MOMENT

— These would be your rooms —
    If you agreed.

A pause — then —

        sound of waves rushing up on a falling body — leaves in a
        great wind — then —

            masts of ships creaking in some harbor. A great
            stone lighthouse with fire burning at the top —
            then —

                the King of Crete made a small gesture
                with his hand — palm upwards — his
                fingers doing a one after the other spread

from pointer to pinkie. A coil of
fern unrolling into the air before
stretching itself out.

Minos was directing Daedalus' eye toward the very large bed dressed
in dark colors. The entirety of the world was in that hand. Made of
that hand. A closing of it could end everything.

The hand hung there open to the ceiling
— if you agree —
the most pregnant of pauses —
a freshwater fish frozen in some mountain lake over winter waiting
for spring to thaw it allow it to reunite with breathing.

Each fingertip a mouth telling a different version of the events.

Stories are a series of rooms — each containing a detail that can be
visited out of order can be reconstructed from memory or changed at
will. The hand of the teller takes these blueprints assembles a house
for the listener to move into.

Daedalus stared at the plans that Talos drew for hours days weeks years. Only understood half of them.

The storyteller's hand wraps lovingly around your neck. Makes eye contact while whispering in your ear.

After Talos died —
                         Suddenly !
                 Mysteriously !
                                  Tragically !
Daedalus released all of his assistants from their contracts brought on younger less experienced apprentices. Ones who wanted to be seen gazing upon a master in hopes of personal gain so they too would be gazed upon.

He would teach them just enough to send them on their way. He would not draw for them. Would not share his secrets. Would not even be seen to build an object around them.

In Daedalus' private studio the unfinished Hermes would whisper the story of Talos' death to any who entered. Daedalus would disassemble reassemble disassemble reassemble the messenger while his apprentices would build trinkets for Athens based on old designs. Daedalus would never understand the parts in his hands.

He learned that he would never be Talos.

That room — the one Talos worked in — had one door no windows a great fireplace. It was full of oil wood metal. Scrolls of drawings.

This room — the bedchamber with Minos in it — had a wide set of doors at one end leading to a balcony overlooking the massive gardens of the palace. Zoe stared out — it was morning the light in Knossos was bleach sharp — the kind of light that doesn't take time to find corners it shafts through darkness moves out of its way or is obliterated.

A murdered darkness begins to drink in its surroundings. Needs so much that it becomes a black hole. One sip at a time it depletes the universe.

— I assume you are going to agree.

Minos is talking.
The question is a formality.
One does not refuse a King.

Daedalus is very good at pretending to listen to these kinds of people. The very wealthy have a need to point out the crystalline edges of their wealth. Show the massive pile of cash without actually opening the curtain to the vault room.

Some will walk you by the recent newest fashionable farthest away acquired things. Others make do with things collected over time. Things ancestors made received acquired and stole.

When an old object is discussed — that is when you discover the type of person they are. The elaborate story showing the might of an ancestor the divinity of lineage — or quick movement to the next thing always with hunger in the eyes. Please please please be impressed. Please.

In that breath you know the depth of the pool you are stepping into.

Anyone could see the hummingbird in Minos' eyes. The boredom once the chase was over. He cared only for the shooting of arrows not the blood and meat on the earth.

When the King gestured towards the bed Daedalus locked his eyes on the royal hand itself — a bed is almost always uninteresting — but a hand detaching from its host to become a perfect floating gesture hanging there like some dumb geography —

well —

Those royal fingers became lines pulling from themselves — elongating wires that thinned wrapped themselves around each other then began drawing connections into the walls.

Streamers of pure gold growing as if from the very nail beds the beds extending into branches into searching tendrils of ivy — growing infinitely quick until piercing the walls of the building unlodging bricks throwing them into the courtyard below. Then branching into the countryside beyond to take over the world leaf there bloom and finally fruit and propagate. The canes would be cut and made into objects. A basket. A stylus. The rocking chair on your grandparents porch where you sat as a child and watched the night come on. Fireflies slowly rising like motes in a bonfire. That magic breathing feeling of earth giving birth to living things.

Stories repeat themselves until the waters are clear then they repeat themselves until the end of the world.

A braided chair that would sit by a hearth in Athens where a young girl would embroider until the night came then she would embroider until her dreams took over and there she would also embroider.

The imagined holes in the wall allowed pinpricks of light to touch the layers of cloth on the bed to reveal jeweled tones there — purplegreen paleblue — within the linen. Daedalus imagined opening a hole in the roof — filling it with reflective metal bringing the full arms of the sun to the inside of the palace. This light lasered the eye leaving violetdark holes burned in his vision.

A linden would grow in that pool of light.

Daedalus would approach the crinkled green of the leaves place one hand on the burls of the trunk. Handholds cankers places to rest oneself. Lindens are instantly wise trees. He would stare until a leaf presented itself and — plucking at the base — would quickly divide the leaf into three parts. He would bind the three fingers in the center of his hand with these thirds then would go about his morning until it was time to draft or direct his builders — he would break each bind randomly

     1

         2

             3

                  then would begin the work.

All is ritual.

When the body stopped kicking.
When it went from person to body.
Talos cold on the sawdust spit of the workroom.

A pinwheel falling through space —
dropped from a tower
trying desperately to make wings for itself.

Then —
shadows —
from those fingers —

Daedalus saw purple lines necrotic spiraling soul leaving the body like a bruise across the floor. Cardinal directions. Cardinal — a pivot hinge — the most important of things in the discussion. A circle of crows.

White ash of burning poplar tree darts flying in from the north

Filigree dripping easterly in copper mercury reflection

South coming in white-capped waves of frothy sea salt

The always refusing western face a closed eyelid only eyelash only

The crows closed around him —

Daedalus — the child — always the child — sobbing as the crows began to tear at his clothing his flesh his eyes. Each placed a stone in a fold of his opened skin then sewed it shut with fibers of feather and thorn. Stones to be carried a lifetime or longer. A weight within him. A grounding wire.

With lines cascading around him — he falls endlessly — a construct of himself collapsing into a basement. The mind constructs the palace within it

>
> the marble towers within it
> the language reaching the sky within it
> a pile of twigs to light on fire.

There in the blackened circle left behind by the burning — there little burnt Daedalus is pressed in from all sides by the wooden boards of dreaming pressed until hardened until hard unpolished a core for everything to wind around.

He awakes covered in cockroaches — not as a child — as an adult. The body of his nephew staring at him with unblinking eyes of slate — silent absorptions. Were there actually cockroaches or were these phantoms of treeshadows in moonlight across him.

What was Zoe doing at the window.

The day was not old enough for the fields to have fully burned themselves of mist the garden would be mysteriously uninteresting. Only the fully seen was worth looking at.

Daedalus sighed accepted the proposed arrangement — live make wonders for the King grow fat have children forever be taken care of like a pet cow. This was a fine place to settle anew. He had decided to leave before he was forced to. Telling Zoe nothing of the late night meeting with the Senator where they refused to say the name of the dead nephew but they only were talking about the dead nephew.

The linden in Daedalus' mind grew yellow — the tips of each leaf wounded. The effect was of a tree on fire. A hot center where a crystalline trunk emptied and refilled while holding aloft a canopy of eternally burning flame.

Five years and some change later he is standing in front of the same palace — precarious Chronos — even for those aware of the head fake of time it comes like sudden fever. The vision of that first day became a tapestry hanging on some wall in some hallway — a symbology for decoding.

The page who came to his door only half an hour before stands at his side. The model of the Thing rested on a small cart covered by a piece of red fabric quickly taken from Zoe's wardrobe. A scarf of some kind — she protested only moments before relenting — vanishing into the back room until they were gone.

Her hand a wave in reverse. A closing of the gesture of Minos that first day. The lines cut from their rootings at the ends of the earth.

Daedalus looks at the sharp angles of the carved stone buildings around him. Clean sand edges of limestone. The whitepink marble lining the upper edges of the buildings is flesh in the saltlight of beaches.

A butterfly object — marble — limestone that has encased itself in earth until it becomes something more. Metamorphic. Alive. A rebirthed thing. The root of the planet itself — dark encased sleeping — under intense desire to be more. Daedalus makes a note to discover where this specific rock comes from. To visit that pit of life. To touch it feel the room beneath the soil.

Beyond the baseline the palace becomes painted in red orange yellow green blue indigo violet. Murals and statues drop their nightclothes showing a shoulder to the rising sun.

The page moves to pick up one end of the cart he looks at the genius waits waits waits. Aware of being watched Daedalus takes a deep breath grabs the other end to begin to carry it up the twenty stairs to the palace doors. The thing is an odd balance between them. They crabwalk. Several out in the morning watch the pair in amusement and fear —

Knossos is aware of the deadline due today.

Two guards stare from the top of the stairs. There is a seriousness about what is coming to the palace but both guards had helped toss Daedalus into the streets those few months ago when the task of the Thing was begun so they struggle to not smile.

Both wait to see if they would be asked to toss him again. One of them will eventually get to toss Daedalus one last time but that is more than 20 years from now.

The page is called Jace. His father a cloth merchant who seems to deal in only low quality fabrics. Whether the man could never catch a break or is a con artist is up for debate. The family would very much like to be of a higher class Jace's father had saved carefully to purchase his son's entry into service of the King hoping Jace's ambition would carry him up the ladder that eventual rising would be a rising for the family as a whole.

Life is not like this. It has happened that a family's fortunes will rise with one of their member's good fortune position appointment or fame. Those sorts of stories are only interesting if that family or person or position or fame or appointment ends. Otherwise it's the least interesting story the world can tell.

Stories all begin their end with a fall — a collapse of the bubble that formed along the way. That pressure finds an escape — surface tension tears just enough — it's held everything up for so long and the scaffolding was built by a writer or bard or whatever and they didn't really know how to weld or nail properly so of course it's all going to come down eventually.

The escaping air tears an ever bigger hole until everything deflates.
A circus tent falling over the audience.
The animals left in their cages wondering what to do.

Jace is bad at this job.

He is unimportant to Daedalus' story but here he is bumbling around opening a door into a hallway that was not his to walk into. Some time — long after this day — Jace does find work that leads to better things. He joins a voyage to the east. He finds himself in the high peaks of the

Andes. He finds himself disappearing into the Kathmandu Valley. There he will become notGreek will happy himself until he never returns.

That story ends in snow — only happens in daylight — a long time from this day. Today Jace is a part of Daedalus' story — this will weigh on both for many years.

The large entry is a mass of Ionic treecolumns. The two men carry the cart to the first set then begin to wheel it deep into the palace. Eyes within the murals watch. They pass no judgment. They do however watch.

Daedalus and Jace cannot see the head of house watching them. They are navigating the room watching the fabric covering the Thing billow like sails. Daedalus thinks about the shape the Thing forms under the fabric —

the plane that its surface creates —

domed here square there a curve of a finger bent with arthritic glee. A moving idea. It has been excavated from within him. Is a part of him.

— Master Daedalus!

Like a pressed flower found in the back of an old book — Ionne's voice is sudden mood. The break of a new season. You know what's coming yet it is still an overnight surprise. Ionne smiles broadly clasps his hands in front of him.

The thing that they don't tell you about Greek architecture is that it is all heightdark blankness waiting to be full. It is not the bleached openness that ruins become. Ionne understands the space well. He is used to filling it to intimidate

indoctrinate
make important
and unimportant
guests
of the Palace.

Jace trips.

His hand sweeps the red cloth from the Thing on the cart.

The fabric is a great crimson owl swooping on a small mouse before it comes to rest on the polished surface of the floor.

From his vantage point at the far end of the room Ionne cannot truly see the Thing on the cart but he feels it. The Thing is a gravity is perhaps the center of a large system of planets. A galaxy eye. It presses. He can feel it becoming a part of him. He suppresses the chill that wants to climb his back. For now he refuses it though he knows that this is a future crawling towards him.

— We are surprised and delighted to see that you have come.

And then Ionne waits.

The two guards watch as Jace hurries to replace the cloth over the Thing. In that glint of red movement is another red movement.

Out in the courtyard beyond the guards a stray dog and a dove are standing on either side of a full loaf of bread — dropped by the woman who takes loaves from the bakery to the palace every morning.

She was in a hurry because she has a katadesmos ready to be folded pierced buried in a grove near the edge of the city. This curse is against a woman named Tretia. The curse is to Hecate. The grove is behind the home of Tretia.

The dove and the dog — are reaching towards an agreement on the bread. Sunrise turns itself fully over into day.

Out behind the palace in the large gardens the peacocks have finished their morning calls begin hunting for small things in the dirt shade to devour.

Somewhere a pearlhide bull kicks at a dry spot of earth the cloud of dust hovers in the air in a moment that stretches out like a cat waking from a nap in the sun. Then the creature looks for a place to lay down.

Minos holds a heel of bread in a thin tawny liquid — the floral wine moves itself into the pockets of air within the morsel — soaks there — tints the whole thing orange peel brown. It is gone into his mouth in an instant.

— He is here.

The attendant nods.

— So he has come to undo what was done.

The King stands. The attendant offers a transparent chiton to cover his nudity. Minos sighs deeply.

— Have him put in the smallest room.

The attendant rushes out.

Minos dresses slowly — tying his belt as intricately as he can. A robe of unwashed linen over top. The King leaves his feet bare — has never will never own a shoe.

An archway opens into his wife's rooms. For five years Pasiphaë has not left the shadows. Minos can see her laying on the couch near the veranda. Can sense her beating heart warm breathing. He stares as he dresses at the pool of fabric that is also a woman that is also his wife.

She is watching the air outside her rooms coalesce around daytime. That her father is the literal sigil of the sun does not comfort her — terrible things occur at daybreak — liminal — the moment where it is seen who did and did not survive the darkness.

She is disappointed to discover this morning that it appears that she — daughter of the sun and sea — wife of Minos of Crete — has survived.

Aware of her husband — of him watching her — even with her back to his rooms — she feels him knows he feels her. After the birth — Asterion — she insisted he would not banish her — jail-like — to hide in rooms across in some abandoned part of the palace. Everyone — especially him — would be made to watch her postpartum. It would be sifted into air like flour while making bread.

Three bee eaters in a row — on the rail of the veranda chit at each other eyeing the garden beyond — cross the sky with their eyes looking for insects. One snaps — quickly a dragonfly appears in its beak. The bird tosses the insect into the air catches it like a ball. The other two hop and noise.

From her position only a sheet of pale bone white sky is seen. She is sure that everything is green beautiful just below but this washed out uniformity calms. She craves the unblemished paper before a writer begins to mar its surface with the thoughts churning their mind. That moment when the air is free of once upon a time.

There is a pain at the back of her scalp. The beaks of birds become three thin iron nails pressing — pokers on the end of a trident.

After all this time — it is still there. Waiting. She can tell what direction the creature is from the pain. It tires her.

When the bull walked from the foam of the sea — no one saw this but it was as true as breathing — this pale apparition demon horrible antecedent of salt made into cowbody — it stood on the beach for three days staring at Knossos. Fiddling crabs tended it — picking algae from its fur shining its hooves with sand — they shone it like hot metal.

One must be prepared to be presented to a King.

She was suspicious of the gift.
Suspicious of its pearlhide size.
Suspicious of the giver of it.

Minos took the gift from the god of the sea as a sign of his own divine lineage inserted it into his own mythmaking — gods recognizing neargods — and he chose to carry that story forward. She recognized the story as part of her own. A story older than humanity. She could read the warning in the hunched shoulders and twisting skin.

That feeling dried to crust on her like sea water on skin.

Poseidon — who must have existed to send such a creature — did not like Minos. Did not like Helios or his children. The Olympian hatred for Titans a wound from eons gone. This Pasiphaë child of a god had made herself small — tried to play mortal. Her brothers — both kings —would be destroyed by their own families. Her sister was cast out a witch became the bad end of a story was exiled would join Jezebel as the image of the evil of women twisted throughout time.

Until the day the white bull made itself known Pasiphaë had managed to hide herself from the knots of fate that wrapped across her bloodline. Had been blissfully detached from the halls of Gods.

But here she could see the strands of fate form before her eyes.

She imagined them being stretched from the distaff freshly sharpened shears being held to the tensing line. Tension there. A waiting. Threads pulled from her corona from the sun halo and golden they became a web to be completely caged by. She would press against them but they would burn her.

Of course Minos fell for this bull.
Of course he promised to sacrifice it at the first feast day after its arrival.
Of course he would not.

It is the oldest story.
        Maybe the only true story.
                Two sides opposed — unable to move an inch.

The war between Titans and Olympus is a cold one. Mutual assured destruction locking things in place. Both sides accepting — little curses — here there — neither side making a true push at annihilation. Everyone is amused for a time. The earth is not rendered in two. For now.

— How deep does the well of Poseidon's curse go.

It is a fester that will build itself a room in the universe. The bullchild Asterion will stand like a jail — invent fear that will radiate outwards into all things. The body will crumble but the cry will be attended to eternally by the subconscious of the planet itself.

Two floors above — like a sesame seed between the teeth — Pasiphaë feels this.

Threads reach out there is a rolling loom. The scent of cedar. Somewhere in the palace Ariadne is dancing in the room Daedalus built for her. In her fingers a dark thread cat's cradles. She is a spider. Threads are coming from within her mouth a spinnerette across her hands coughing up winedark thread. Smiling all the while.

Pasiphaë thinks of her sister banished to the edges of civilization. She thinks of the stories of Circe turning men into pigs — imagines pigs on a spit — imagines them as pets — smiles for the first time in days mentally begins a letter to that far off place no one dares to visit.

Months into months.

A feast day approached Minos found a bull close in size to the pearlhide that Poseidon had sent them. From her rooms she watched a group of loyal men good men cover the brown bull in a paste of chalk mixed with olive oil. They rubbed this into the bullflesh — massaged — ignored no parts.

She knew what was coming.

She lit a candle sent word to her siblings that she knew her time was coming.

She stood on a balcony staring into the sun unafraid of the burn telling her father who ignored her as stars have always ignored those that walk beneath them.

None replied though all received the message — lamps of scented oil were lit in response — a hush as all waited for the crack of water across glass.

On the day of her birth Pasiphaë's mother Perse went to the waters edge then into the water until she felt her body release from earth's grasp. The first time she had returned to the sea since the pregnancy began. There under the unblinking eye of Helios Perse gave birth to their second daughter. Pasiphaë's first breath was warm noontime salt.

In the sky above her father the sun turned the horses of his chariot loose allowed his disc of fire to spin in place for one full hour. The sun became white then its edges unfolded as if made of paper revealing the many-colored universe within — it was night inside the sun — vast expanse of stars opened — connected themselves in patterns unknown until that moment. A kaleidoscope rained down upon the earth in oozing pear-shaped drops. The horses of Helios galloped freely in the sky leaving dark holes in the canopy. Helios himself sat cross-legged in the center of the opening sun invented mediation as he pondered all that was happening below and all that would happen ever until the end.

Perse sat in the water allowing her daughter to breathe sea until the materials of afterbirth — shards of sand that had fused into glass — has dispersed into all the waters of the globe. Then she stood abruptly held the daughter upside down and brought forth Pasiphaë's first cry with a firm smack to the ass.

Pasiphaë was kept from the water. They called it a compromise — Helios and Perse — but what could the water being do in the face of the sun. She was dried by his gaze.

Helios feared his children would disperse as foam. Their inner waters would burst their skin until boiling outward. They hid from rain from water — it wasn't until her fifteenth year that Pasiphaë knew that water could be touched without a fear of death.

On that birthday Pasiphaë walked to the land around the small whitewashed mud hut her and the other children of Helios and Perse called home. Helios had built this — placed it on a rolling expanse of rock-filled land far from the sea — surrounded it with sheep orchards. The children would grow attended by these things — the occasional traveler or person seeking worship.

At fifteen Pasiphaë stood on the highest point. Watched the land turn colors under the shadows cast by clouds that were hiding her father from her view. She walked for ten days arrived at a cliff face. Below the sea boil thundered. Shaken to her core Pasiphaë jumped.

Perse gave birth to four children of Helios and never spoke to one.

They killed the chalked bull on the sandstone altar meant for Poseidon's pearlhide. Blood ran sickly thin stank of meat. It filled the eddies in the soil around the base of the altar — congealed into jelly was consumed by wasps.

That night the earthquake came.

There was a crack in the sound — swarm of cicadas baked olive like smoke at the temples expanding out into fields on feast days. If anyone had been watching they would have seen a great tear pull itself open at the far edge of the palace gardens. From within — the sound of cicadas became actual cicadas pouring forth crossing the fields with purpose for the palace. The swarm grew bodily through openings in the palace walls — into Pasiphaë's rooms. She was surrounded by the liquid cloud of hundreds screaming then the hundreds landed on her skin in her hair glued themselves to her eyes went quiet.

The silence they emitted froze her like a statue.

— *ewwwes were told wwwere saids to giving up ones selfs pasiphaë ewwwes wwwere a god* —

Cicada voice.
Dry husk corn voice.
Too many to distinguish voice.
The echo a reverb. Her skin rose in bumps. The kind of cold that comes after swimming in summer.

— *doesnt matters this is wwwhats goings to happen ewwwes wwwill bare a child* —

The voice was in her head — had always been there — would always be there. Noise of the sea as her body plunged into it. The noise of it at her eardrums. The quickening darkness of the waves the lessening of color the blue. She could feel the creatures acting as one creature — as a thing — rubbing legs together combing themself preparing to lift her from the floor toss her from the windows.

> — *ewwwes wwwere told wwwere saids to pasiphaë*
> *ewwwes wwwere a god and ewwwes wwwent to*
> *minos as creatures dos to slaughter*
>   *hes*
>   *unwwworthy —*

She feared opening her mouth. They would slide into her take possession of her. She would cease to exist.

> — *his bloodsline wwwill again* —

A sound of rustling. The edgepain of three hot irons pressing into the base of her skull — a trident of cicada legs reaching into her cerebellum turning their keys making her a toy.

— i have delivereds the message asked of i.

Thousands of smallnesses lifting at once. The sound of all the pages of Alexandria's great Musaeum burning.

The room was dark. Her skin took on a tint of purple as if she was bruised head to toe as if she was dying from lack of oxygen. She glowed in the dark. Her heart was blue it pumped flight need — wings beating in a cage — bees at the neck of a flower rolling in pollen — the grasp of a beak on a living dragonfly.

Her hair smelled of salt. Was wet with what could have been sweat.

Asterion cries like a jail in his room unattended.

The stinging at the base of her skull. Sudden desire.

How high is the water.
What temperature.
Is the bottom visible.

At what point does the boiling become commonplace enough to be put up with.

Minos leaves the fuzzing of their sleeping chambers.

Daedalus sits on a chair with an elaborately curved back. Jace on a second identical chair some feet away. Between them the Thing under its red shroud.

They are small men in a small room.

Alabaster marble etched across with thin veins of hard-boiled egg yolk yellowgreen gray moving just under translucence. It makes Daedalus seasick.

Beyond there are doorways into hallways into a maze-like expanse of more doors hallways rooms with marble more doors. Columns painted rust yellow green blue. A mural painted onto the wall between the two doors has Minos' mother led to the glowing hills of Crete by Zeus himself in his goldenwhite bull form attended by leucist peafowl. One holds in its beak a lantern glowing with the amber sheen of the sun.

That bloodline.

Daedalus allows himself one moment to think about the implications. Allows himself to recognize the inevitable tree inside the seed.

One moment.

When Daedalus contrived to find the body. He made sure a young apprentice was with him wideeyed shaking sleep from himself in the thin morning light. The child dropped the papers he was carrying — the stream of time ceased — went backwards — became a flow from sea to mountain then from mountain to the core of the earth. Daedalus saw the boy turn into a child an infant a wombsac — the threads were turning back into wool into sheep.

A thief!
In the night!
From some court in some foreign power.
Attempting to get at the secrets of the great workshop of Daedalus.
No one could see the things broken or stolen. Nothing had been

disturbed. Except the body of Talos. His bones looking like the spread wings of a bird shot through with an arrow.

The scandal the endless sympathetic visitations. Everyone fell over themselves to believe. No one even began to form the obvious question.

The deception was a fragility — a crack in the ceramic that would eventually allow everything to flow outwards. Even though no questions arose — the Thing was there waiting to be known.

The morning after the feast where Minos sacrificed a bull but not the correct bull the city of Knossos was checking itself for damage after earthquake. A minor rumble — some stones were off center animals were spooked one old man had a heart attack died in his evening chair. He had been reading news from family in Athens. It appeared that the great city was bothered by Minos' desire for power. They were thinking of taking action. That action was a small army being trained intensely.

In a field at the edge of the palace garden a guard named Lander inspected the strange slash that opened in the night. The usual hum of birds replaced by gentle grasssound. Birds and cats know when the land is unsafe — they vanish from it.

Earth had lowered — receded as a tide in seconds — revealing a toothy grin of dirt and rock one hundred yards in length. From above it is the curve of a thumbnail moon the horns of a bull tipped in silver placed on a banquet table with plums olives a cheese of unknown origin. At first light Ionne had told the night guards they could not leave until the fields had all been checked until this new feature had been inspected the pearlhide bull found safe.

Lander and the others drew lots.

Small yellow purple white flowers dot the field. This open land was left wild by Minos for his strange bull to graze. Talk among the guards was that the bull was not a bull that it was a god an ancestor of Minos brought to flesh. Things believed become true. No one was to touch the pearlhide bull. None wanted to.

There was no sight of the creature.

Where the tear happened it appeared that half of the land had lowered while the other half rose to touch the air leaving a gape. The field had something to say. It would say it.

Masses of exposed roots reached their glowworm tendrils into the air were sunbaking at this very moment. In days they would turn brown hard against oxygen. The roots held on to rocks and other objects they had stolen from the earth. A shattered clay pot a silvered mirror one thin rib bone.

At the center a dark space blinked opening into the underground that had always been there.

Lander's body tensed as he took one step trying to see into the depths.

Does one in this moment go back tell the head of house risking being pulled into a full investigation — or investigate lightly to hopefully pass the full probing off to others receive a nice pat on the head.

In his mind Lander formed the shape of an obol turned it on its axis as if deciding a bet with himself. It spun on its edge refusing to land either face or tail. Even his mind was against him this morning.

Lander walked to the opening. The ground crumbling unstable the sound of water below the smell of the filthy ferryman mixing with salt and muck. All gives way. He falls

        into darkness — a sort of rabbit hole endless cold Lander
        stripped bare by the reaching roots — fingers knowing
        fingers — taking cleaning
            his skin of all its properties — readying him
        for the first footfall into Hades.

Ashen dark. Scent of warm skin. Lander stares into the bleakness the bleakness stares back. The Acheron lapping at ash making eddies in the crunched bones of those refused crossing. He checked his pockets — Lander did not have coin — he would join the layers of soil under foot.

His xyston reached into the dark. Lander as far in the light of day as one could be while doing this work. The long weapon met rock but continued to be swallowed by the hungry earth until Lander stood face to face with the threshold shaking.

Beyond the light — where Lander cannot see — rustling — a great beast shuffling along stone hallways. Hunger. There is only more within.

A more that shimmers with heatstroke. A more that is unfathomable. The field becomes a mist then a great stone plaza. A terrace facing Lander. Steps staring at where he stands. He can see the faces of Knossos dressed in pressed white. They look at him. At the open mouth of earth behind him. Their faces are broken. There is a line of children wearing laurels. They are being led to the opening. Are marched by Lander into the underworld one by one. They are

crying

in

the room

that is the world.

Minos stands. Lander cannot see his eyes. Pasiphaë is there next to him. She is staring into the earth for the 1000th time. Daedalus there refusing to blink. Others Lander does not know. Each and every one swallowed by what they see.

A drumbeat and the underworld eats.

This is too much. He is too small. He begins to pull the xyston back there is a great sucking rumbling as the ground vomits mud floods out breathing wrapped in the smell of doom. Eyes of fire teeth whiter than anything possible. Phobos alive burning. Lander is engulfed by the thick.

There is a kind of moment where time pulls focus from the events at hand. Where thresholds loosen doors hang open. When someone is dying and on oxygen. When the young are very young are doubling in size every day.

Peacocks call at dawn.

The largest of Minos' twenty leucist peacocks observes the sky. Still as a statue on the worn stone orb at the top of a garden staircase the bird has its back to the dawn.

The peacock is disturbed by its lack of desire to call to the sun. Is confused by its own silence.

In the east end of the palace are a set of doors — if you agree — waxed to nearblack carved with great beasts in the Egyptian style. These doors had come from a King of Egypt as a gift were a thing Minos enjoyed showing to guests. In fact had shown to Daedalus and Zoe on the morning that he offered these rooms to them. If they would only agree to his terms. Now — decades from now — they sleep in that room in that bed.

The esteem of Kings is not assured. It pulls itself up runs off to the next bigbrightthing. It is a magpie looking for colored foil. If it would even follow the phases of a moon it would be more sound.

This dawn was the morning of a new moon. Black moon. The star in the sky abandoned by Selene and her chariot.

Auspicious.

Terrible things occur at daybreak. When you see who has and has not survived the night.

In the chambers on the other side of the door the family of Daedalus slept.

Icarus sixteen in his bedchamber dreamt of an open field of glowing poppies. Dreamt of running in them faster than feet can carry.

Iapyx on his back. The dead patient from a few days before sat on his chest watching him sleep.

Iapyx's wife Photine dreamt of a journey far away that would culminate in a pregnancy.

Zoe felt the empty place where her husband should be. At the balcony Daedalus paced. It was barely morning. Though there was no mist. The gardens must look beautiful.

This is where the obol stops spinning choses itself then lands on one of its sides.

One sharp rap at the door is all it takes.

Those moments. When the young age before your eyes. That feeling. The phone rings you just know that it's your mother calling to tell you your father is dead at sea. That your sister has decided to marry and leave the house. That everything is covered in dark fabrics already.

There is a bulge in that waxed wood.

The servant moves to open the door. The inventor raises his hand slightly to stop the boy but it is too late. Has always been too late.

The door heaves. A lung taking in too much air — blisters — cracks

— finally — light finds its way through all of that density like a fire that was starved but not out.

Lander is on his back. Mud pouring a watershed a fall and catch. Unable to breathe — Lander becomes momentarily paused.

Something about Daedalus — he is a walking dissociation. Now — this group of soldiers — one of them at the door to the palace the day of the Thing who also threw Daedalus into the street before the Thing was made. These soldiers. The family assembled in their nakedness.

One by one before Daedalus' eyes — murdered before the dawning sky. Until Icarus. Who was bound dragged from the room thrown — crying — into a jail-like room atop the time keeping tower that looked like a finger pointing into the sky.

That Daedalus had been pacing had known what the dawn was bringing. That he told no one but had whispered it into the sky at the first bleed of sun.

That the words had drifted to the ears of a white peacock about to call morning to life.

That those words paused the peacock where it stood.

Daedalus had given Ariadne the key to the Thing. Had explained the path to the center. Gave the secret of the gears of the underworld. Had helped the blood-covered son of Athens stinking of bull and man out of the hole in the Earth. He then covered for and watched a ship sail into early morning darkness carrying the daughter of Minos and her new husband until his eyes were crusted over in salt.

The cataracts of creation.

A repeating circle. He had caused the birth — Asterion — had conceived built broken the Thing — all for null. Somewhere a water god laughed until a whirlpool consumed an armada. Ariadne would be murdered within the week her new husband off on other adventures.

Sound of blood absorbing into the fabric of the rugs. The slash across their throats spilling cockroaches. You could see the stones in Zoe's skin. She was silent throughout. She was unkind in her gaze unblinking. She knew that Daedalus would be spared. She stared at him until the life in her was gone. Then continued staring.

Minos only came after — made a sharp sucking sound with his teeth

— Do you think the gods
            wrote our story before we even met. Do you suppose
            that the ending of it was known
                        at the birth of our ancestors.

Daedalus was blinded in one eye because he had the vision of the Thing. His dominant hand broken because he had drawn up one too many
            plans.
Each finger dislocated because they built a cowbody out of wood for Pasiphaë.

His tongue removed for singing his ideas across Athens and Knossos.
Given only bread brought from a small bakery in Athens where Zoe
    once worked.
Locked in a tower with his youngest son to remind him of Asterion.
Melting the candles down and making a suit of feathers.

One sucking breath.
Full of dirt and stone.

Lander falls to the ground his spear vanishing into the earth. The faucet of soil now a breathing over him with razorhooves. The face of fear turns its gaze to the small man. The pearlhide bull covered in ash mud blood stinking of stagnant water. Those black too human eyes scanning Lander — the beast knew what Lander knew. It nodded in that shared knowledge. Accepted that this was fate working around them.

It refused to be touched for weeks. It did not eat or drink water. The tear in the earth was fenced off ignored cursed. None would go to the pearlhide again but it roamed the fields of Knossos a phantom creature growing ever wilder.

Daedalus and Zoe were there the night of the quake. First night in the new rooms that they would have for four years. They awoke in the night with the shaking. They questioned the path they had chosen. Daedalus assured Zoe that this was fine and true.

He went to the desk in the front room. He looked over the list of things. The King wanted much — a tower to tell time — ways to make him more godlike — new ways to wage war to find a control over Athens — new means of farming.

Practical and obscene.

Daedalus sketched each quickly next to the description. Made lists of tools needed. The people needed. He mapped out the projects one by one made himself steps to take so the path would be clear sure sane.

Quickly a small but elaborate workshop was built in old stables. A team of draftsmen builders creatives assembled. Over the next four years the tower was built on the edge of town facing Athens to ward against the rumors — a small open room at the top for observing the sea — new chariots were designed — new methods of quarrying rock — a new aqueduct system.

Much of that was done after the birth of the King's youngest son. Asterion — who even now cries in his jail-like room.

The last thing — the Thing — that Daedalus would build for Minos sat on its cart covered in red while also buried in the earth beneath the mouth the earthquake opened.

— My inventor.

Minos sweeps into the room unannounced. The layers of his fine robes catching light they swirl it around his flesh making it appear that he moves with the speed of water not on feet but will alone.

The two small men stand after a second of collecting themselves.

    — I hear you have something for me.

3. HER THREADS SPUN

This morning it appears that Pasiphaë has survived.

The disappointment is physical. A deep pain in her chest.

Unattended — Asterion cries — in his jail-like room.

> For two —
> five —
> eight years.

When he was born — nine months after the unslaughter of the pearlhide bull but twenty years before the very real slaughter of Daedalus' family — the horror in the room was a heavy wool blanket covered in the down of poplar seeds. A smother — you would imagine it putting all flames out — imagine it sending ashcloud into the air. The wrongness in that thought. After minutes — hours — days even — the heat would burst the wool would become a sheet of flame moving like water across all of Crete until everything was undone.

Pasiphaë struggled labor for two days. The icy feel of it passing through her again

again

again.

She would not make a noise only whisper pleas to her father that he would make this right take it away undo the entirety of history creation itself. That perhaps she of all her siblings would be spared the coming on of Poseidon's curses against her family.

Helios — the sun — keeping with his character — refused to even glance in the direction of Crete. She was no longer his to watch after.

Rest would come only because her body was too tired to hold itself awake — even then she would dream of labor — awake then exhausted then — a repeating process. When it was over she collapsed slept erased herself from existence.

The baby was
                was   it   was
           was it   it
   was fire —

      a hum inside it — oxygen waiting
      to remind itself that it too has a body.

Stories collect themselves orbit around the consuming gluttony like moths without mouths.

The cicadas had left a feeling of sunburn all over her body that would never leave her. She was not bruised but she was red. A lifetime of bathing in her birthwaters would not undo the feeling. She itched in her flesh stared at the field where the pearlhide bull wandered. An urge to go to it.

Why would she.
Why wouldn't she.

A gap here — stories melt in the heat of the mind of the teller. They are not to be seen at once but in fragments presented like bits of a broken mug. Held together with a ribbon of gold. There is a tradition of reassembling broken things. There is a succession of speakers who craft the universe that we all live in every day.

It comes difficult
       difficult
           difficult
   for everyone.

Somewhere Ariadne is seventeen holds a spool of twine her eyes dissociate her fingers numb before the mouth of the earth where Asterion rages in his room-jail. She is also a child dancing on a rotating wood floor that Daedalus built for her directly above the first jail-like room where Asterion was caged before he was caged.

As she dances her family and Daedalus' family watch. They have come inside from the blasting sun. From the ritual of sending children into the earth to be destroyed by what lies beneath.

     She is dancing.

          Minos watches out of habit.
          Her feet on the polished wood the floor
          itself tilting beneath her movements. The
          room breathing in with her. The sorcery
          of thread between her fingers — catching
          each groove of her palm. Becoming a knit.
          A knowledge of its own.

          Between the dancing threads

                    Minos sees.

          In flashes — cut scenes — in the
          negative shapes of Ariadne's arms
          and the floor.

          Whole lives are coming — uncoming there.

Daedalus in hiding in an eastern kingdom.
Hiding and tinkering. Making arts for others. The
exact same arts. Repeating everything in a slightly
different meter.

That ruler's harem has taken him in. He makes toys.
Small things to amuse. He is loved quiet has grown a
beard is gray with age. While he works he mouths a
name Minos doesn't know.

Years later a hooded man comes to the gates of the kingdom
claiming he knows of Daedalus that he is owed a penance. The
harem fools him inside. Pours boiling oil on him in his sleep.

It is himself. His flesh melting into the piles of pillow. Minos the
King of Crete taken to the quick. Dumped into the trash like the
burnt bones of an animal.

As Ariadne spins she contrives an end to things with a boy she does not love but does find useful.

Moirai.
Chronos.
Youth. Mother. Crone.

They conspire in the mid of night. In cracked groutfilled spaces between moments they are there plotting silently under foot just outside peripheral vision. Old man with a pendulum for arms swinging belling himself at every second. The three-in-one holding shears a scratch of mothy thread. At certain times the heartbeat in the wrists — there for whatever biological reason — will tick with their machinations. Will — under your pillow at night — keep you awake with the reminder of them.

For some this knowledge is wonderful is a thing to press against to seek out the rough hewn edges attempt to find ways to the other side of. Those kinds of people will allow their fingertips to shred on the surface of the knowledge to fray.

For others it is a thing to avoid. To run from.

There by the far bank of Ascheron. There. Clotho squats collects handfulls of the ash burned from the soles of the feet touching the harsh earth of the underworld. In her hands a length of yarn forms from her working she places this on the distaff of the moon the yarn then spins on the wheel of the celestial dome.

Distaff to spindle drawn pulled along the length of the earth measured in crooked knuckle lengths Lachesis will count endlessly as she walks the edge where water falls into space. Her robes the idea of the color of the memory of night.

Then the undead one Atropos with shears muddied in sticky black shut to anyone other than herself will move along the length testing the burls in the fiber feeling for the one notch that longs for the blades. Then the sound of closing heard only by the newborn and the dying — a metal rod run along the cracked edge of a ceramic bowl.

Women birth and unbirth. Find the spaces to exist around the things that are not allowed to them fill those spaces hold them in secret. Cupped hands whispered held shut released as fireflies into the dark parts of the forest.

Two nights after the earthquake the sacrifice of the bull — but not the right bull — Pasiphaë stood in the field watching the pearlhide closely.

Nightair stung the places her skin was not covered. Her body had carried her here seemingly in her sleep had brought her to this spot woken her made her open her eyes see stare into the night. The tear in the earth before her. The hollow breath of the earth flowing from the gaping mouth.

She could feel all of it.

This was the curse coming real like foam across sand. It allowed her to wake to know that it was coming to see it on the horizon. Low green line burning on the surface of the sea — flash — swimming — saltfilled echo of a borealis.

Little to be done — she went to bed.

Her mind turned in place — gyro — orrery — unloosed molecules.
                              Tick.
              Tick.
                       Tick.

Pasiphaë would insist on being watched at all hours. Followed. The servants of the palace became exhausted by her complained they spoke about her descending into madness. The healers were called. Pasiphaë's humors mapped. Her biles deemed unbalanced.

They changed her bedding. Repositioned her furniture. Suggested she take a trip or move rooms. A new coat of whitewash was applied to the walls in her chambers. Things were cleansed as if there had been a death.

Pasiphaë contained her frustrations until the healers left. Then she stared out into the fields kept to herself demanded her attendants keep close.

She would go to the inventor.

Rumors of the Queen passed as contagion about the city. A handshake was all it took. Even being near to one with the words on their tongue was enough to wake in the night with chills and the word in the folds of brain.

Madness.

Zoe sat on a chair on the balcony outside their rooms a cup of cool honeyed wine in her hand. She had been drawing the gardens the peacocks the way the light was hitting the water in the fountain.

— I don't believe it.
And neither should you.

She tossed a heel of bread to the garden below. Peacocks moved on it quickly.

The note from the Queen calling Daedalus to her rooms was short not up for debate.

Ionne will collect you. Bring nothing.

Decision making. One second in the mind often over before one realizes there was a crossroad in front of them. A moment where the story could have gone a very different way.

Zoe's first child is five years away. Her second three years after that. Her second child is also her last. They are already collected within her. Energies forming from Zoe's cells. Silent becoming.

Difficult that Zoe couldn't possibly know these things. People are trapped in the now unable to really see the nonlinear connections going outward from one body to other bodies. That ripple on water effect of turning this corner today that one tomorrow. She knew enough to suggest ignoring the letter. She could see the death in it.

Five years later — while Daedalus is presenting to Minos — standing with Jace in that small room. Pulling the red scarf back ta daa! Zoe sits in darkness pregnant waiting for things to right themselves knowing that right is no longer there to be had.

Where gods live among nongods the stories hold a constant third person view. The people narrate their own lives coldly moving around events. A spinning event with one audience. The gods
    watching watching watching watching watching
    always.

Two peacocks held the heel of bread and pulled on it resembling dogs with a length of rope. Sudden jerks pulls the looping of necks eyes locked on each other blazing. Mechanical. Because it was a heel the bread refused to give. The peacock to the northwest pulled to the right quickly the one to the southeast countered with a sudden head bob neck recoil. Both had their wings extended. Both males with fans of feathers for tails folded inward like rolled carpet. Their crests bobbing violently.

Northwest planted its legs began to walk backwards. Southeast did the same. They formed the shape of an hourglass.

The bread would not give.

— I want you to build me something. A thing.

The room — one of those inexplicable rooms. A place where chairs wait for something to occur.

Pasiphaë was pale. Her skin nearly glowed in the darkened room. She wore too many layers of linen. They competed for attention made her arms and head seem to have come detached from its body. There were faint dark lines pulsing outwards from her into the cosmos. Her skin — blue tinged — veins standing upright on the surface it prickled and rose in goosebumps that itched. She was not a being of the land. She had come into her sea.

— I am not proud to ask this.

She nodded to a small table between their chairs. To the square of paper there.

— I will not say these things aloud.

Her voice was calm water completely at odds with her appearance. The catastrophe of her became a shell of protection the clouds reaching out from the hollow center of a hurricane. Too steady — you could set a boat into it it would not drift from the spot placed. You could sit there for weeks and starve in that voice.

A bell rung in the distance. The nearby temple or a servant call. The room did not have any windows the sound snaked itself through hallways around columns to get here to enter the skull and vibrate at the frequency to cause the brain to hear it.

Daedalus removed the small seal unfolded the paper. Katadesmos A clean handwriting — the Queen's own — calligraphy as mood.

— I will have your wife killed if this is not done quickly in secret.

The daughter of a sea witch and the sun.

It would be open at the rear. Barbaric. Wood metal gears with human flesh sat at its core.

Daedalus at his workbench staring at the description of the thing in the Queen's script. The first of two things Daedalus would build that he could not — would not — name.

I will have you killed if this is not done is what she had said. In that monotone that was without inflection but sparkled with the light on a not yet frozen winter lake.

The house of Minos demands things unearthly but wholly of the earth at once.

— What is this thing that you draw so poorly uncle.

Talos

stood in front of Daedalus.
On the far side of the workbench.
Ash and smoke pouring off him.

The workshop was dark. One candle illuminating only the spot directly in front of Daedalus the sphere of the immediate drawing. Only the rough sketch of the thing to be worn like a shroud. The phantom Talos — or real creature Talos — rested its head on its hands like a damned child wanting an obol to buy candy.

Elbows on the surface of the bench. It had a smile eyes were pools of white swirling with bluegreenviolet. Talos the undead here to ask questions.

Do you meet the eyes of the dead. Do you avert them. Toss the candle into the face of it and run.

— I died with two coins in my pocket uncle.

I am allowed two trips.

My hands are as solid as yours.

Feel them.

Talos thrust his hands in front of his uncle. Daedalus saw the lines on the flesh — puffy with water — white from lack of sun — but flesh with all the things that come with it. Daedalus saw the lines tumble from the fingers land like thread from a needle on the workbench as if the blood itself were being spun. Mounds of wool spilled from man to bench covering the papers there.

Daedalus refused.

Talos hit the workbench with one clenched fist. The surface jumped the sound became the room. A cloud of ash ballooned above the two men. The undead man snatched the Queen's paper.

— I could do this thing. Could make it more real than even she could wish. More real than the statues that walked. More real than real uncle.

The beacons of light shaped as they were like the eyes of a dead nephew. One could become a suicide in them. The way he said uncle was a spell. A curse that should have remained folded buried.

Difficult.
Decision making.

The signs always there. Crossroad arrows pointing in all directions. Always there never seen. A cross of hands.

Evil — there is no evil but — evil does bargains at the crossroads. On bridges. In liminal spaces. Places where reality catches — a great mist arises obscuring delineations the shoulders of the road become fuzzy. So easy to go out of bounds. There is always a sharp drop on the other side of the berm.

The inbetween. When you are neither there nor here. In that space nothing is truly alive reaching the next end is a potential surprise. A potential erasing of existence.

Talos leaned into the circle of light the skin that was not skin caught the colors of fire became years of nacre layered over years — everything was thin membrane over the skinned hindquarters of a cow. Purple moving. The undersides of eyelids. Milk. Blood. Pus. Fat.

His smile was a dog pulling its lips back in anger or happiness. The smell of moss mold the underside of rocks. The knowledge in that smell. That of standing on a bank of hot ash tinged red with iron. The rust ash that was bone. The knowledge of standing there in bare feet melting like wax waiting for a ferry to come and take the body to another shore of even hotter redder ash.

The water a swirl of foamy fat. The face of the ferryman a clockface that refused.

Daedalus leaned back instinctively — feeling gravity within himself. That moment of knowledge that things outside you hold sway over you. A baby crying endlessly — jail-like — never realizing that the people who have left the room did not in fact cease to exist.

Or did they.

A tweaking pull pinch fabric in hands tugging leaning leaning leaning falling.

Talos didn't even bother to laugh.

You don't disagree with the dead.

A decision was made without being made. A path chosen. Reaching into her bag of yarn Lachesis pulled the one for Daedalus quietly made a knot. Her long fingers with the razoredge nails stained streaking the color of slate lingered always there. A touch point. Her fingers felt along the yarn folding into itself felt the fold knew then the wires that were spiraling outward in both directions. She nodded to herself.

Things clicked together creatures not born yet had knots formed in their threads as well.

— This —

will —

— hurt.

Talos held his uncle's hands to the workbench surface as vices do wood. Dead things are not meant to touch living things. His fingernails becoming clawlike thorns tipped with the poison of the underworld. Ash poured from the world of the undead through Talos' mouth into Daedalus' screaming mouth. A Pompeii of self. Every pore of the living man turned at once inward plugged itself black lost cohesion exploded into monstrosity that was then sealed within itself. The places where Talos collected turned light absorbing black. A void in the room a suck. The skin too tauthard over the meat. Tension seeks the weak spot. Daedalus was all weakness.

Talos flowed filling every space where Daedalus was.
Hands.
      Fingertips.
            Eyes.
The splitting. Flesh into ribbons floating on the slight air of the room. Daedalus turned to blood mist dissipated settled as a red dew on the floor. Talos. Alive once more ready to build.

The candle went out — all that could be heard — scratching graphite on paper.

Minos stared into the thin walls of the model of the Thing. The red scarf in Daedalus' hand expectancy around everything. The reveal a sort of anti moment.

— And it would be dug out of the place in the fields where the teeth rose in the quake.

The men agreed on the excavation. The becoming alive of the Thing.

— What will we do with the bull then...

Daedalus looked at the king of Crete suggested that it could be placed in the Thing as the first offering.

Minos nodded.

Daedalus watched the room condense. Watched as Pasiphaë took her robes off — climbed into the hollow beast he had built but not actually built. He watched the room open into night become field the idea of fields he had seen before. A sort of compass rose of fields.

He positioned himself under a tree stood sentry like he knew what was to come though he did not. Inventors are very good at seeing the moment they are in. They are not so good at seeing beyond it.

Within the court of the field Pasiphaë controlled the cowbody. Everything was damp. She felt it in her skin. The itch there the legs of the cicadas there the prick of the trident there. The world smelled of sea. The breeze was seagod's laughter.

She felt she was a child hiding under a table. That was how the movement was done. A slidecrawl inside the beast. Handles for hands loops for feet. A shufflecrawl across the grass.

When Pasiphaë was a child living with her brothers and sister she would hide under the table when the storms came. They came often on that exposed rock place that Helios placed the hut for his children. Circe loved the attention from the sky. She would stand under it dare the lightning to strike her. Aeëtes and Perses were protective they wearily watched for signs that the gods were coming for them as they knew they would.

Denied air and sea — they grew with the lambs that wooled about the hut. They learned them. Taught themselves to shear feed. Made clothing. Took the offerings from the cults left for their father for themselves. Those strangely robed figures — faceless — humorless — coming to their remote isolation with foodstuffs piles of fabrics at the dawns of new seasons.

Under that table — dark with use — small — she would huddle tell herself stories of the world beyond hers. Water stories of monsters in the deep. Of kingdoms of sea people making space in conches sandbars the giant suckers of an octopus. Her sister — greenly real and with her. Brushing her hair telling her it would be all right the gales would not take the house down not ever.

Of the air she imagined flying on bird wings. Of towers lifting into clouds the giants that lived there. The horses pulling the sun wheel across the sky. Her hands at the massive gold leads as a new god of light. One who would look at the creatures below. Her hair a blaze of fire spiraling into nebulae. Her father — not real — but the very idea of light hovering behind her. Both of them laughing.

She went naked into the cowbody. Oddly silent. She had been afraid that the thing would be loud with its metal wood joints. With her inside efforting. But once she was there it all seemed to become flesh. Move of its own will. Her will that was also the will of Poseidon.

Her intent was the pearlhide bull. That itch that had been placed inside her — not hers — a need that was forced on her. It sat there rooted. She could feel it winding around her heart a yard waiting to be knit she could do nothing against it.

She thought about Leda.

Near the earth mouth. The place the earthquake had unsettled. The start-end of all of this. The bull stood. It was waiting for her.

> Inevitable
> inevitable
> inevitable.

> Gods are stupid
> cruel
> stories that should not exist.

The undoing was so obvious in it but Daedalus reached out a hand pulled the oiled cloth away from the largeness of the cowbody. It came fast. A fully rendered beast. Wood metal oiled.

Covered in hide of pure white.

She stared at the thing. More real than she wanted. Fearful real.

— It's —

The two of them — The Queen and the Inventor — stood staring at the thing that had been made.

    — so real.

She touched the head where the snout was where her own head would go.

She could not breathe. The room smelled of rot ash.

Daedalus had been in a trance for a month. Every time he had entered the workshop he vanished and Talos took over. Now he blinked in the darkness. The thing before him unknown autofiction even though it was made with his hands.

— I am terrified.

Lachesis pulled her threads spun them around her fingers preparing the knot.

Then she was stood in the field — knelt really — hunched — on all fours crawling within the false cow. Moving towards the pearlhide bull.

In every atom Pasiphaë knows the horizon to the east pitches towards astronomical twilight.

Zoe sits in the darkness of her room waiting for her husband to return from presenting his Thing to his King. Pregnancy pain in her back.

Her hands press into the dough of a life not lived. The counter covered in softness. The fire raging. The bakery left to her after the family she worked for moved away or died or had no children of their own who wanted it. Zoe the baker.

A cloud of flour releases into the air.

She oils the dough into a large ball places it into a crock to settle rise. She slices the already made loaves. The baby within her — Iapyx — the first. Icarus will be later though she can also feel his arms forming within her. Iapyx kicks is testing out the lengths of the womb. Wanting to run into the world and find it. She places her hand there feels the pad of the foot. Understands what it is to be a thing with a thing inside.

She is a housing and he is driving her towards motherhood.

The bakery is busy real
somewhere
because she has thought then told it to the air.
She has desired it.
But she knows this dream.
Has had it before. And it shifts —

Iapyx will be a doctor will marry will have children be forgotten to history. Icarus will die — his father will make the wings from the feathers of the roosting birds in the tower. Will melt candles for wax. Will put them into shape and place that first creation on Icarus' shoulders. Then Daedalus will go about making a second set for himself.

Stories can change.

This one — Daedalus and what he has done. Something to explain it to be said that was then cut and left out —

> For all his flawed ego Daedalus loved Zoe. He could not see or understand a life where the lines from her body did not meet and knot with the lines from his own. The tangle a series of fishing lines or yarns that had been thrown to the elements until they hedged themselves — became one. At this moment he saw his fortunes as being also hers.

> He did love her. And he made note to say it the next time he saw her.

But he will not. He will not even as he buries his son.

Icarus' body was in the water around the shallows of the island. All skin wax sinew feather bone. All blood unclosing eyes thread.

Two arms bent the wrong way.

Two wings fused to his back.

What if the gods are not real but are enough in the mind to cause paths to be set. What if creators become real only after being spoken of enough.

Daedalus buried two of his creations. His uncrying face darkens ash begins to pour from his open mouth into the grave. It fills the hole becomes a pack around the broken mess of Icarus. The ash drifts up a reverse snow. Each turns into an ashen-colored partridge with an upside down bleeding heart on their chest. Then they are gone.

The sun is trapped in its sphere unrising. The machines are stopped. Here's a small flowering tree that Pasiphaë once sat under. Dogwood. The bitters make a tea.

The flowers are one of the firsts of a new year. You can make jam and vodka from the version named Cornelian Cherry. Pasiphaë knew these things — more — about the plants around the palace. But she had removed herself from this field and every other field ever since the pearlhide came.

Over near the earthmouth it is watching. Heaving. The beast had been running in the early hours. The universe is breathless and unmoving. Will be for as long as it takes.

Pasiphaë nods. Is nodding.

The tree changes into a twisted olive then an ancient plane. All gently scenting the air as if it had never been scented before. The bark peels with age and an eon later a tour group stands in the rubble of the palace taking photos with their phones. A different similar tree casts a small shade on them.

The world seems to have become a floating tree with a few square feet around its base.

The story with a secret — it moves like the tides. No matter the story — the ending the same. The storyteller — a multiple of itself. A generational inheritance. A rope with enough length to hang an entire tribe with.

Lachesis knots the thread. Or does not —

because she may or may not exist.

Now. Not then.

Pasiphaë is aware that her husband has left to meet Daedalus. She is aware of the things about to occur in another room of this palace on this morning 5 years after the earthquake and the bull and the birth of her final child.

She glides towards the railing. Bee eaters unaware of her. One holding the glossy blue of a dragonfly in its beak.

Quickness.

Not a virtue — more of a skill. Silence the same. Her hand strongly out then back to her side. The other bee eaters — flashes of their bright green blue red soft butteryellow melting into the strengthening sun leaving one alone in her grasp.

She turns it to face her. The coals of its eyes gloss metal in rain. The dragonfly — still alive — she reaches her fingers plucks gently at it takes it from the beak. — examines it — then places it to her tongue swallowing it whole.

She whispers two words into the morning light. They drift into the warming air towards the unblinking eye of her father. A spell that binds everything on the island around her. If she is to succumb to Poseidon's will then so will everyone under the gaze of the gilded sun-like roof of the palace.

Mutual destruction.

The bee eater — released — flies into the day to tell stories of this to others. Warn them off the railings of the palace.

Pasiphaë looks out beyond the gardens to where Poseidon's pealhide bull grazes. Where she herself will graze within the cowboy Daedalus builds for her. She stares into the face of the bull of Crete.

She sees Minos staring back.

All stories end with eyes open realizing all they have taken in and trying and failing to look away before the final words can come. Even though they are on the verge of overeating. They cannot yet close. All stories end with the image of everything everywhere etched over the retina.

The eye is unable to stop itself.

In another place a pile of feathers prepares itself.
A pot of beeswax prepares itself.
A sea prepares to eat a second son.
A bull leaper runs grabbing the horns somersaulting over the back of a bull.
A matador prepares a sword while a bull huffs with three banderillas in its back.

Statues crack on their pedestals bury themselves in sand the future prepares itself to be made on the crumbling bones of the past.

Zoe drops her waters — goes into labor.

Michael J. Wilson has two collections of poetry, *If Any Gods Lived* and *A Child of Storm*. He lives in Santa Fe, New Mexico, where he helps craft immersive story experiences for Meow Wolf.

CPSIA information can be obtained
at www.ICGtesting.com
Printed in the USA
JSHW060024260723
45394JS00002B/37

9 781960 451019